Back to Basics

ENGLISH

for 8-9 year olds

Sheila Lane and Marion Kemp

Grammar

| Nouns are the names of people, places and things. | Ordinary names are called **common nouns.** e.g. girl   bird | Special names are called **proper nouns.** e.g. Janet   France |

Read the **common** and **proper nouns** in the box.

| man   Paris   Angela   boy   country   James Wilson   town   Canada   baby   Smith doctor   America   city   Australia   village |

 Write each noun under the correct heading.

Common nouns of people	Proper nouns of people	Common nouns of places	Proper nouns of places

A **proper noun** always begins with a **capital letter**.

 Write these sentences with a capital letter to begin each **proper noun**.

1 lyn's pen-friend lives in denmark.

_____

2 The river thames flows through london.

_____

3 tokyo is the capital of japan.

_____

Alphabetical order

✏️ Write the missing vowels in the alphabet.

___ b c d ___ f g h ___ j k l m n ___ p q r s t ___ v w x y z

✏️ Write each set of nouns in **alphabetical order**.

Common nouns	**Proper nouns**
pansy _____	Washington _____
violet _____	Rome _____
rose _____	Moscow _____
lily _____	Berlin _____

> When more than one word in a set begins   a **n** t
> with the **same** letter, you need to look   a **p** e
> at the **second** letter of the word.   a **s** s

✏️ Write each set of common nouns in **alphabetical order**.

bee _____	pony _____	sow _____
bat _____	pig _____	seal _____
bull _____	puma _____	swan _____
boar _____	panda _____	stag _____

✏️ Write each set of proper nouns in **alphabetical order**.

Monica _____	Smith _____	Algeria _____
Michael _____	Adams _____	Africa _____
Martin _____	White _____	Australia _____
Myra _____	Brown _____	America _____

abcdefghijklmnopqrstuvwxyz

English usage

and	but
Use the word **and** to link ideas in a sentence which are the **same**. e.g. Sugar is sweet **and** honey is sweet too.	Use the word **but** when the ideas in a sentence are **different**. e.g. Sugar is sweet, **but** lemons are sour.

Write **and** or **but** in each sentence.

1 Giants are big, _____ dwarfs are small.

2 Jane rode her bicycle _____ Tim rode a bicycle too.

3 Peter was quick, _____ Paul was much quicker.

4 The sun gives light _____ the moon gives light too.

5 A rabbit has a soft coat, _____ a hedgehog's coat is prickly.

because
Use the word **because** to tell **why** something happens. e.g. I could not read my book **because** it was too dark.

Write each sentence giving the best reason.

1 Tom was sent to bed because
- it was time to get up.
- it was tea-time.
- it was after 9 o'clock.

_____

2 Lisa couldn't reach the shelf because
- her hands were wet.
- it was too high.
- she had a headache.

_____

3 I put on my warm coat because
- it was cold.
- it was so hot.
- the sun was shining.

_____

Spelling

'**Silent e**' makes the short vowel sound in the middle of a word have a long sound.

> I hate my new hat.

Say...p<u>i</u>p
and p<u>i</u>pe

Say...w<u>i</u>n
and w<u>i</u>ne

Say...t<u>a</u>p
and t<u>a</u>pe

Change the short vowels to long vowels by adding
'**silent e**' to each word.

tub <u>tube</u>   pin _____   hop _____   mat _____

cub _____   bit _____   rod _____   pan _____

Write the correct word from the box in each sentence.

| not note |
You are _____ playing the right _____ .

| slid slide |
I _____ down the _____ in the park.

| cap cape |
I wore a _____ on my head and a _____ round my shoulders.

| hid hide |
When we played _____-and-seek, I _____ in the tree.

| mad made |
She was _____ when I _____ a mistake!

'**Silent e**' words lose the '**e**' at the end when '**-ing**' is added.

e.g. hope   ride   care
     hoping   riding   caring

Add **-ing** to these words:

bite <u>biting</u>   hate _____   love _____

note _____   make _____   ride _____

⟨5⟩

Comprehension

Read these questions:

   1 Where do Cleaner fish live?

   2 Why are Cleaner fish called Little Dentists?

Find the answers to the questions in this information:

> Cleaner fish are only 10cms long. They live in the warm water of the Indian Ocean.
>
>   Cleaner fish clean the teeth of bigger fish. They swim into the mouths of bigger fish and poke out scraps of old food from between the teeth of the larger fish with their long, thin, pointed noses. This is why Cleaner fish are sometimes called the 'Little Dentists of the Ocean'.

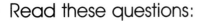 Write the answers in the sentences.

   1 Cleaner fish live in _____

_____

   2 Cleaner fish are called Little Dentists because _____

_____

_____

 Write true or not true at the end of each sentence.

   1 Cleaner fish are about 100cms long. [ ]

   2 Cleaner fish clean the tails of bigger fish. [ ]

   3 They swim into the mouths of bigger fish. [ ]

   4 Their noses are short and stubby. [ ]

Which is it?

Do you write **here** or **hear?**

Here means...in this place.	**Hear** means...to h ⟨ear⟩ with your ⟨ear.⟩
e.g. Come **here** at once.	e.g. Can you **hear** the birds singing?

 Complete these sentences with **here** or **hear**.

1 I have lived _____ for three years.

2 Deaf people can't _____ .

3 Did you _____ what I said?

4 Stand _____ until you _____ the whistle.

5 I didn't come _____ to _____ that kind of noise.

6 If I _____ any more unkind words, I shan't stay

_____ for another moment.

Do you write **there** or **their?**

There means...in that place.	**Their** means...belonging to them.
e.g. Look over **there**.	e.g. The children lost **their** shoes.

 Complete these sentences with **there** or **their**.

1 I waited _____ until my mother arrived.

2 Everyone enjoyed _____ visit to the Zoo.

3 _____ is the library.

4 Don't go over _____ because the ground is muddy.

5 The children left _____ coats over _____ .

6 _____ house is over _____ by the pond.

Punctuation

This is a **full stop**: An ordinary sentence begins with a capital letter and ends with a full stop.

Write these 3 sentences with correct punctuation.

on tuesday morning the firebell rang all the children walked quietly to the door later their teacher checked their names on the register

_____

_____

_____

_____

This is a **question mark**: A sentence which asks a question ends with a question mark.

Write these sentences with a **full stop** or a **question mark** at the end of each one.

1 Where do you live _____

2 I am eight years old _____

3 My hair is brown _____

4 Why are you crying _____

Write a question for each of these answers:

1 _____ It is seven o'clock.

2 _____ My sister's name is Susan.

3 _____ I left it at school.

4 _____ The answer is ten.

Capital letters

A C E G I K M O Q S U W Y
B D F H J L N P R T V X Z

A sentence begins with a **capital** letter.

Write these sentences correctly:

1 come and eat your tea. 1 _____

2 don't make a noise. 2 _____

3 please shut the door. 3 _____

A proper noun, such as someone's name, begins with a **capital** letter.

Carl   Macadam
Marion   Khan

Write these names correctly:

george _____   singh _____   alan _____

helen _____   johnson _____   betty _____

A proper noun, such as the name of a place, begins with a **capital** letter.

Queensland   Toronto
Mount Everest

Write these sentences correctly:

1 paris is the capital city of france _____

2 the river darling is in australia _____

3 spain and italy are in europe _____

Remember!

Easter   April | Friday

Proper nouns, which are **special** names, begin with **capital** letters.

Christmas   September

Spelling

Look carefully at the **number words** on the card.

eleven	11	_eleven_	✓
twelve	12	_____	☐
twenty	20	_____	☐
eighty	80	_____	☐
hundred	100	_____	☐
thousand	1,000	_____	☐

Cover the words on the card with a small piece of paper.
Write each number as a word.
Take the paper away and check your spelling with ✓ or ✗ .

1	2	3	4	5
LOOK	**SAY**	**COVER**	**WRITE**	**CHECK**

This is a way to learn to spell correctly.

Use **LOOK SAY COVER WRITE CHECK** for these words:

one	1	_____	☐
eye		_____	☐
leaf		_____	☐
boy		_____	☐
thumb		_____	☐
glove		_____	☐

Write each number word correctly.

heigt _____   eetthirn _____

Questions

We ask a **question** when we want to find something out. Question sentences begin with a capital letter and end with a question mark.

Read the sentences in the box.

My name is Jackie.	How old are you?
What's your name?	I'm eight years old.
Where do you live?	When is your birthday?

 Write each sentence from the box which asks a **question**. Write an answer for each one.

Questions   **Answers**

1 _____   _____

2 _____   _____

3 _____   _____

4 _____   _____

Write these jumbled words to make sensible **questions**:

1 what the is time   _____

2 are you going where   _____

3 far is it how   _____

4 when you coming are   _____

5 was that who   _____

6 late you are why   _____

7 pen your which is   _____

8 broke who the cup   _____

Masculine and feminine

Some nouns are **masculine**	Some nouns are **feminine**	Some nouns can be masculine **or** feminine
e.g. man	e.g. woman	e.g. baby

Read the nouns in the box.

boy	uncle	cousin	son	child
mother	daughter	aunt	person	girl
father	toddler	grandfather	grandmother	grandchild

Write the nouns in the box under these headings:

Masculine   **Feminine**   **Masculine or feminine**

_____   _____   _____

_____   _____   _____

_____   _____   _____

_____   _____   _____

_____   _____   _____

Write these sentences changing all the **masculine** nouns to **feminine** nouns.

1 My father has two sons. _____

2 The twin babies are brothers.

_____

3 A king's son is called a prince.

_____

4 The boy helped the old man across the road.

_____

5 Grandfather Jones is my uncle's father.

_____

Comprehension

Read these questions:

Write | yes | or | no | or | don't know | after each one.

1 Do zebras have striped bodies? ☐ ☐

2 Do zebras have hooves? ☐ ☐

3 Are zebras members of the cat family? ☐ ☐

4 Do zebras live in Africa? ☐ ☐

Read this true information:

Zebras live in Africa. They belong to the horse family.
Like horses, zebras eat grass and have strong hooves.
Unlike horses, zebras have striped bodies. A zebra's
stripes are black and white.
Zebras live in herds. There are many family groups in
each herd. A zebra family is made up of a male stallion,
four or five mares and their young foals.

Mark your | yes | and | no | answers with a | ✓ | or | ✗ | .

Answer these questions in sentences:

1 What do zebras eat?

_____

2 What colours are zebras' stripes?

_____

3 What is a male zebra called?

_____

4 What is a young zebra called?

_____

Looking at words

These two words t o They have **different**
have the **same** sound: t w o meanings and spellings.

Say each pair of words to yourself:

for	right	see	pear	stare	rain	whole
four	write	sea	pair	stair	rein	hole

 Complete each sentence with the correct word from the box.

1 Children learn to read and _____ .

2 The opposite of left is _____ .

3 Two and two make _____ .

4 I ate an egg _____ breakfast.

5 A _____ is a sweet, juicy fruit.

6 A _____ is a set of two.

Read these clues for the puzzle. Fill in the answers.

1 To use your eyes

2 The salt water which covers the earth

3 Water falling in drops from the sky

4 A narrow strap for guiding a horse

5 A kind of step

6 To look hard at someone or something

7 A complete thing

8 A kind of opening

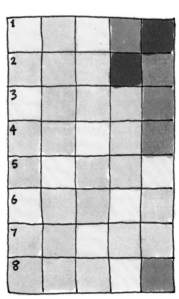

English usage

who	which
Use the word **who** for **people**.	Use the word **which** for **things**.
e.g. This is the **boy who** won the prize.	e.g. This is the **book which** was on the shelf.

Complete these sentences using **who** or **which**.

1 I picked up the pen _____ was on the floor.

2 I fell over my brother _____ was sitting on the floor.

3 I tripped over the cat _____ ran into the room.

4 I gave her the money _____ was in my pocket.

5 I spoke to the postman _____ was standing on the step.

Write these sentences using the correct ending:

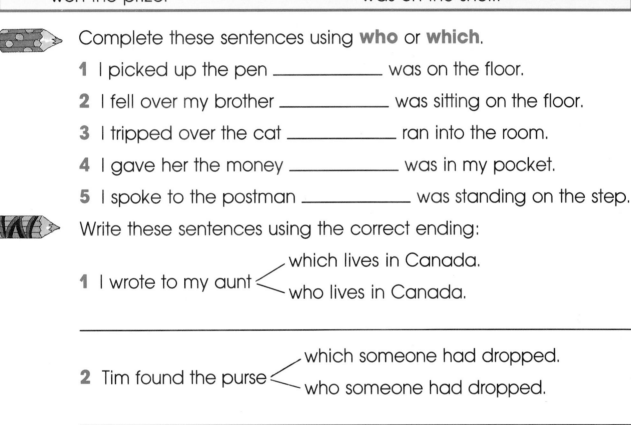

1 I wrote to my aunt
which lives in Canada.
who lives in Canada.

_____

2 Tim found the purse
which someone had dropped.
who someone had dropped.

_____

3 Mary undid the parcel
which was for her birthday.
who was for her birthday.

_____

4 We went over the bridge
which crossed the railway line.
who crossed the railway line.

_____

 Write a sentence of your own using **who**.

_____

 Write a sentence of your own using **which**.

_____

Using a dictionary

The words in dictionaries are arranged in alphabetical order.

Write the words for the pictures.

Write the words in alphabetical order.

s _ _

s _ _ _ _

s _ _ _ _ _

s _ _ _ _

s _ _ _ _

1 _____

2 _____

3 _____

4 _____

5 _____

Write the word in each set which comes **first** in the dictionary.

1 toe
  tie _____
  tap

2 pile
  pale _____
  pole

3 rude
  ride _____
  rode

4 feel
  foal _____
  fail

5 sing
  song _____
  sang

6 winter
  wonder_____
  wander

Arrange the words in the box in alphabetical order.

Look up the meaning of each word in your dictionary and write it here.

vow

vulgar

veil

vacant

view

_____   _____

_____   _____

_____   _____

_____   _____

_____   _____

Spelling

e e   These pairs of vowels **look different**, but they can make the **same sound**.

(e e) as in f**ee**t
(e a) as in l**ea**f

Write (ee) or (ea) in each of these words:

c l _ _ n   s l _ _ p   _ _ g l e   n _ _ t

s h _ _ p   s p _ _ k   b _ _ k   s _ _ t

_ _ c h   t _ _ c h   s t r _ _ t   _ _ s y

(e a)
(e a)   These pairs of vowels **look the same**, but they can make **different sounds**.

(e a) as in l**ea**f
(e a) as in h**ea**d

Say the words in the box aloud.

heavy	health	beast
beam	bread	steal
feather	east	deaf

Write the words from the box in two sets.

(ea) as in leaf
_____
_____
_____
_____
_____

(ea) as in head
_____
_____
_____
_____
_____

Write the answers in the puzzle.

1 You can sit on this

2 The opposite of west

3 A kind of road

4 People who can't hear are this

5 This animal has a fleece

6 The king of birds

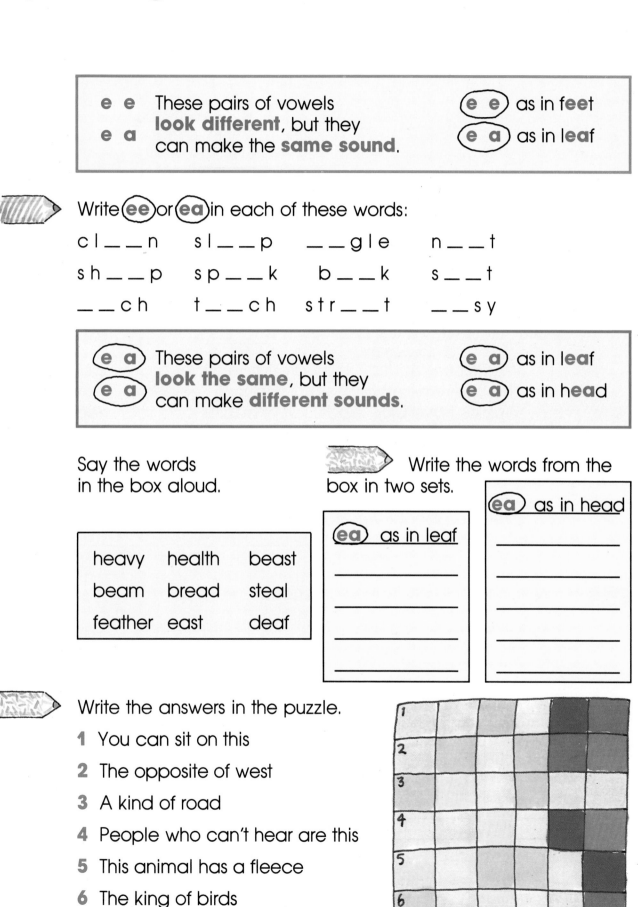

Comprehension

Read these questions:

1 Which animal weighs more, a whale or an elephant?

2 Which animal can swim under water with its mouth open without drowning?

Find the answers to the questions in this information:

Whales are not fish. They are large water mammals. The Blue Whale weighs more than 30 elephants. Whales have big heads, large bodies and tails shaped like triangles. A whale's mouth is not joined to its air pipe. This means that a whale can swim under water with its mouth open without drowning. Whales breathe through their blow holes and come up to breathe about every 15 minutes.

Write the answers in the sentences.

1 A _____ weighs more than an _____ .

2 A _____ can swim under water with its mouth open without drowning.

Write yes or no after each question.

1 Are whales fish? ☐

2 Are whales mammals? ☐

3 Do whales have triangular tails? ☐

4 Do whales come up to breathe every 2 minutes? ☐

Spelling

The letters (o w) can make two different sounds.

Listen to the sound of (o w) when you say crown.

Listen to the sound of (o w) when you say snow.

Read the words in the box.

blow	slow	yellow	know	grow
crowd	frown	tomorrow	follow	brown

Fill in the missing letters for (o w) words.

1 The opposite of fast is _ _ow.

2 _ _ow_ is a dark colour.

3 A large number of people is a _ _ow_.

4 To _ _ow is to get bigger.

5 To wrinkle your forehead is to _ _ow_.

6 A _ _ow is a hard knock.

7 _ _ _ _ow is a pale colour.

8 To _ _ _ _ow is to go after someone or something.

Use *LOOK SAY COVER WRITE CHECK* for these words:

flower   _____ ☐

snowball   _____ ☐

crown   _____ ☐

window   _____ ☐

pillow   _____ ☐

clown   _____ ☐

Grammar

Words which tell us what is being done in a sentence are called **verbs**.   e.g. I **washed** my hands.

Choose the best **verb** from the brackets and write the complete sentence.

1 The ship (walked, sailed, swam) on the sea.

_____

2 The children (drank, chewed, read) their books.

_____

3 A bus (arrived, sang, wrote) at the bus stop.

_____

Read these **verbs**:

washed	barked	watched	swooped
played	scampered	purred	brushed

Write the **verbs** from the box in the sentences.

1 The dog _____ but the cat _____.

2 She _____ her face and _____ her hair.

3 We _____ television and _____ a card game.

4 The owl _____ down, but the mouse _____ away.

What can **you** do?

Write these **verbs** in separate words: seeheartouchtastesmell

_____ _____ _____ _____ _____

What can **worms** do?

Write these **verbs** in separate words:
wrigglesquirmstretchwiggletwist

_____ _____ _____ _____ _____

Singular and plural

Singular means **one** of anything.

one fork   a spoon

Plural means **more than one**.

two fork**s**   some spoon**s**

The letter **s** is usually added to the noun when there are more than one.

Add the letter **s** to make **plural** nouns.

1 an egg: six _____
2 one car: two _____
3 one girl: twin _____

4 a bird: a flock of _____
5 an apple: lots of _____
6 a boy: some _____

Write the following phrases with the correct word from the brackets:

1 a pair of (shoe, shoes) _____
2 one new (pencil, pencils) _____
3 a library of (book, books) _____
4 the forest of (tree, trees) _____
5 an old (chair, chairs) _____

The letters (-es) are added to the plurals of nouns which end with (-ch) (-sh) (-s) (-ss) or (-x.)

Add (-es) to make **plural** nouns.

1 a torch: two _____
2 the box: six _____
3 my address: their _____

4 an atlas: a set of _____
5 one princess: three _____
6 the witch: many _____

Comparisons

When you **compare** two things, you say what is the **same** or what is **alike** about them.

hot means:
'giving off heat'

a **fire** is:
'a mass of burning material'

comparison: as **hot** as **fire**

 Draw a line to match the words in the two lists which are **alike** in some way.

List A	List B	Write the comparisons here:
as cold	as ABC	_____
as soft	as ice	_____
as easy	as grass	_____
as green	as lead	_____
as heavy	as silk	_____

 Draw a ring round the word in the brackets which makes the best **comparison**.

1 as hard as (bread, iron, cheese)

2 as straight as an (river, road, arrow)

3 as graceful as a (swan, pig, elephant)

4 as wise as an (sheep, owl, chicken)

5 as sharp as a (needle, pencil, crayon)

Write your own **comparisons**.

as white as _____   as quiet as _____

as bright as _____   as happy as _____

as slow as _____   as light as _____

Comprehension

Read these questions:

Write ⬚yes⬚ or ⬚no⬚ or ⬚don't know⬚ after each one.

1   Is the sun a big star?
2   Are all stars the same size?
3   Is the sun the biggest star of all?
4   Are some stars smaller than the sun?

Read this true information:

> The sun is one of many stars in the sky. It is over a
> million kilometres across and seems very large to
> people on earth.
>   There are other stars in the sky which are bigger
> than the sun. These are the giants and super giants.
> Stars which are smaller than the sun are called dwarfs.
>   The sun gives light and warmth to the earth.
> This light and warmth is necessary to make plants grow.

Mark your ⬚yes⬚ and ⬚no⬚ answers with a ⬚✓⬚ or ⬚✗⬚

Answer these questions in sentences:

1   What is the distance across the sun?

_____

2   What are the stars which are bigger than the sun called?

_____

3   What are stars which are smaller than the sun called?

_____

4   Why is the sun necessary to life on earth?

_____

Spelling

These vowels can make **one** sound:

oa e.g. b**oa**   **oi** e.g. **oi**l   **ou** e.g. l**ou**d

Complete one word in each sentence with **oa**, **oi** or **ou**.

1 I wear a c__ __t in cold weather.

2 The singular of mice is m__ __se.

3 Is the kettle b__ __ling yet?

4 Show the way by p__ __nting your finger.

5 What a l__ __d noise the drum makes.

6 The fishing b__ __t sailed out to sea.

7 Wash your face with s__ __p and water.

8 A f__ __ntain of water spurted up from the lake.

9 Choir boys have good singing v__ __ces.

10 I f__ __nd an old map in the treasure chest.

Use *LOOK SAY COVER WRITE CHECK* for these words:

numbers _____ ☐

letters _____ ☐

wheels _____ ☐

colours _____ ☐

fruits _____ ☐

vegetables _____ ☐

Missing words

Read **all** the words in each sentence and in each set of brackets.
Choose the best word from the brackets to complete each sentence.

1   The aeroplane flew up into the sky and _____ the town. { by / over / down }

2   The children ran _____ the winning post. { off / away / to }

3   I like sausages, _____ I don't like minced meat. { nor / both / but }

4   The cat drank the milk _____ it was thirsty. { why / how / because }

5   _____ neatly in your new book. { Walk / Write / Swim }

6   I clean my _____ with a toothbrush. { hair / shoes / teeth }

The **clue** to the missing word in each of these sentences is in the meaning of the sentence itself.
Read **all** of the sentence.
Write the best word you can think of in each space.

1   Two, four, six and eight are all even _____ .

2   Red, yellow, blue and green are all _____ .

3   Most cars have four _____ , but bicycles have only two.

4   Peas, beans and cabbages are the names of _____ .

5   Favourite _____ are apples, oranges and pears.

6   The _____ C and D come after the letters A and B in the alphabet.

Grammar

> **Adjectives** are words which **describe nouns**.
>
> e.g. the **bright** light
> a **wild**, **stormy** sea

sweet	brave	deep	juicy	dark
bright	short	angry	fluffy	sharp

Write **adjectives** from the box which
best describe the nouns.

1 I cut my finger on the _____ knife.

2 The _____ dog barked furiously.

3 Rabbits have _____ , _____ tails.

4 A _____ star shone in the _____ sky.

5 I ate a _____ , _____ apple.

6 The _____ man dived into the _____ water.

Write an **adjective** of your own choice
to describe each noun.

1 a _____ flower   2 a _____ sky

3 a _____ orange   4 a _____ tower

5 a _____ sea   6 a _____ fire

Write a noun of your own choice
for each adjective.

1 a fat _____   4 an enormous _____

2 a tiny _____   5 a beautiful _____

3 an ugly _____   6 a miserable _____

Looking at words

Opposite means **one** of **two** things which are completely **different**.

e.g. a **happy** face   a **miserable** face

Write adjectives which have **opposite** meanings to:

rich _____   high _____   fat _____

weak _____   new _____   dirty _____

Write each sentence giving an **opposite** meaning to the underlined words.

1   Give the child a <u>new</u>, <u>sharp</u> pair of scissors.

_____

2   The clown had a <u>large</u>, <u>jolly</u> face.

_____

3   A <u>tall</u>, <u>dark</u> stranger came to the door.

_____

Similar means of the **same** sort.   *speed race* (run) *rush dash*   All these words have **similar** meanings.

Write verbs having **similar** meanings to:

talk _____   move _____   eat _____

see _____   shout _____   hit _____

Write each sentence giving a word of **similar** meaning to the one underlined.

1   The children <u>rushed</u> to the door.

_____

2   "Stop <u>chattering</u>," said the teacher.

_____

3   "<u>Clean</u> your hands at once," said their mother.

_____

Singular and plural

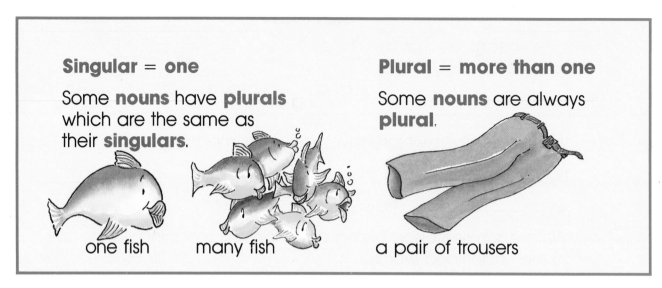

Singular = one

Some **nouns** have **plurals** which are the same as their **singulars**.

one fish   many fish

Plural = more than one

Some **nouns** are always **plural**.

a pair of trousers

 Underline the correct **noun** in these sentences:

1 The (sheeps, sheep) were on their way to the field.

2 I am wearing my new (spectacles, spectacle).

3 Both the (cat, cats) ran up the tree.

4 This pair of (scissor, scissors) is blunt.

5 The herd of (deers, deer) stood on the hillside.

6 I could see two (church, churches) in the distance.

Do you write **was** or **were**?

Use the word **was** for **one** person or thing.	Use the word **were** for **more than one**.

 Underline the correct use of **was** or **were** in each sentence.

1 When the last cow (were, was) milked, all the animals (was, were) taken back to their field.

2 The teacher (was, were) pleased because all the children (was, were) early for school.

3 Tim and Tom (was, were) scared because the story (was, were) about a ghost.

Spelling

> These sets of letters can often
> be found at the beginning of words:
>
> scr- e.g. **scrape**
> str- e.g. **strip**

Make complete words by writing **scr-** or **str-**
at the beginning. **Say** each word as you write.

_ _ _ing   _ _ _ibble   _ _ _ong   _ _ _amble

_ _ _ub   _ _ _etch   _ _ _ange   _ _ _ipe

Complete the words in each of the following
with **scr-** or **str-**:

1   The cat played with the ball of _ _ _ing.

2   _ _ _eams were coming from the excited children.

3   The floor was littered with the _ _ _aps of paper.

4   I _ _ _etched my arms and reached the bar.

> These sets of letters can often
> be found at the end of words:
>
> -dge e.g. e**dge**
> -tch e.g. i**tch**

Make complete words by writing **-dge** or **-tch** at the end.
Say each word as you write.

wa_ _ _   le_ _ _   wi_ _ _   do_ _ _

he_ _ _   sna_ _ _   we_ _ _   swi_ _ _

Use *LOOK SAY COVER WRITE CHECK* for each of these words:

badge   _____   ☐

watch   _____   ☐

strap   _____   ☐

screw   _____   ☐

straw   _____   ☐

Missing words

The clue to the missing word in each of these sentences is in the meaning of the sentence itself.

 Write the **one** word from the box which makes sense in the sentence.

1 | jersey white
snowy you | I wear a _____ in cold weather.

2 | burst flags
blue we | The _____ blew in the wind.

3 | us soft
fly birds | All _____ have feathers.

4 | look brown
eyes two | We see with our _____ .

Draw a ring round the **one** word which would **not** make sense in the sentence. Choose a correct **one** to write in.

1 | plants trees
bushes red | The _____ are losing their leaves.

2 | friend sister
called aunt | My _____ knocked at the door.

3 | rain down
snow hail | The _____ fell from the sky.

4 | rabbit's cat's
playing dog's | The _____ name is Spot.

Draw a ring round **all** the words which would make sense in the sentence. Choose **one** to write in.

1 | yellow sun
moon sets | The _____ shines in the sky.

2 | fast watch
clock when | A _____ tells the time.

3 | children hats
people use | All _____ have brains.

4 | paint pen
pencil pretty | We use a _____ for writing.

5 | pages words
good pictures | Books have _____ .

6 | egg orange
drink apple | I ate an _____ because I was hungry.

Looking at words

Each of these pairs of words has the **same sound**, but a **different meaning** and **spelling**.

 Write each sentence using the correct word from the brackets.

1 The red and $\begin{Bmatrix} \text{blue} \\ \text{blew} \end{Bmatrix}$ flag $\begin{Bmatrix} \text{blue} \\ \text{blew} \end{Bmatrix}$ in the breeze.

_____

2 $\begin{Bmatrix} \text{Eye} \\ \text{I} \end{Bmatrix}$ spy with my little $\begin{Bmatrix} \text{eye} \\ \text{I} \end{Bmatrix}$.

_____

3 Ronnie $\begin{Bmatrix} \text{eight} \\ \text{ate} \end{Bmatrix}$ $\begin{Bmatrix} \text{ate} \\ \text{eight} \end{Bmatrix}$ green apples.

_____

These pairs of words have different spellings but end with the same sound. We say that they **rhyme**. Say them aloud and **listen** to the **rhymes**.

 Make pairs of **rhymes** from the box like this:

four ✓	come	said	night
bed	meet	bear	hum
bite	hair	seat	door ✓

 Complete this playground rhyme: 'Each, peach, pear, _____
Out goes Tom Thumb.'

Answers

P2
man	Wilson	country	Paris
doctor	Angela	town	America
baby	James	city	Australia
boy	Smith	village	Canada

1 Lyn, Denmark
2 Thames, London
3 Tokyo, Japan

P3
lily	Berlin
pansy	Moscow
rose	Rome
violet	Washington

bat	panda	seal
bee	pig	sow
boar	pony	stag
bull	puma	swan

Martin	Adams	Africa
Michael	Brown	Algeria
Monica	Smith	America
Myra	White	Australia

P4
1 but 2 and 3 but 4 and 5 but

1 it was after 9 o'clock.
2 it was too high.
3 it was cold.

P5
cube pine bite hope rode mate pane

not, note
slid, slide
cap, cape
hide, hid
mad, made
noting hating making loving riding

P6
1 the Indian Ocean.
2 they clean the teeth of bigger fish.

1 not true 2 not true 3 true 4 not true

P7
1 here 3 hear 5 here, hear
2 hear 4 here, hear 6 hear, here

1 there 3 There 5 their, there
2 their 4 there 6 Their, there

P8
On Tuesday ... All the children ... Later ...

1? 2. 3. 4?

1 What time is it?
2 What is your sister's name?
3 Where is your _?
4 What does _ and _ make?

P9
1 Come...
2 Don't...
3 Please...

George Singh Alan Helen Johnson Betty

1 Paris France.
2 Darling Australia.
3 Spain Italy Europe.

P10
eight thirteen

P11
1 What's your name?
      My name is Jackie.
2 Where do you live?
      I live in ....
3 How old are you?
      I'm eight years old.
4 When is your birthday?
      My birthday is on ....

1 What is the time?
2 Where are you going?
3 How far is it?
4 When are you coming?
5 Who was that?
6 Why are you late?
7 Which is your pen?
8 Who broke the cup?

P12
boy	mother	toddler
father	daughter	cousin
uncle	aunt	person
grandfather	grandmother	child
son	girl	grandchild

1 mother, daughters
2 sisters
3 queen's, daughter, princess
4 girl, woman
5 Grandmother, aunt's, mother

P13
1 Zebras eat grass.
2 Zebras stripes are black and white.
3 A male zebra is called a stallion.
4 A young zebra is called a foal.

P14
1 write 3 four 5 pear
2 right 4 for 6 pair

1 see 3 rain 5 stair 7 whole
2 sea 4 rein 6 stare 8 hole

P15
1 which 2 who 3 which 4 which 5 who
1 who 2 which 3 which 4 which

P16
saw shell spider stamp swan

1 tap 2 pale 3 ride 4 fail 5 sang 6 wander

vacant veil view vow vulgar

P17
clean	sleep	eagle	neat
sheep	speak	beak	seat
each	teach	street	easy

beam	heavy
east	feather
beast	health
steal	bread
	deaf

1 seat 2 east 3 street 4 deaf
5 sheep 6 eagle

P18
1 whale, elephant 2 whale

1 no 2 yes 3 yes 4 no

P19
1 slow 3 crowd 5 frown 7 Yellow
2 Brown 4 grow 6 blow 8 follow

P20
1 sailed 2 read 3 arrived

1 barked, purred
2 washed, brushed
3 watched, played
4 swooped, scampered

see hear touch taste smell
wriggle squirm stretch wiggle twist

P21
1 eggs 3 girls 5 apples
2 cars 4 birds 6 boys

1 shoes 2 pencil 3 books 4 trees
5 chair

1 torches 3 addresses 5 princesses
2 boxes 4 atlases 6 witches

P22
as cold as ice
as soft as silk
as easy as ABC
as green as grass
as heavy as lead

1 iron 2 arrow 3 swan 4 owl 5 needle

P23
1 The sun is over a million kilometres across.
2 They are called giants and super giants.
3 They are called dwarfs.
4 It gives light and warmth which is
necessary to make plants grow.

P24
1 coat	5 load	9 voices
2 mouse	6 boat	10 found
3 boiling	7 soap	
4 pointing	8 fountain	

P25
1 over 2 to 3 but 4 because
5 Write 6 teeth

1 numbers 2 colours 3 wheels
4 vegetables 5 fruits 6 letter

P26
1 sharp 2 angry 3 short, fluffy
4 bright, dark 5 sweet, juicy 6 brave, deep

P28
1 sheep 2 spectacles 3 cats
4 scissors 5 deer 6 churches

1 was, were 2 was, were 3 were, was

P29
string scribble strong scramble
scrub stretch strange stripe

1 string 2 Screams 3 scraps 4 stretched

watch ledge witch dodge
hedge snatch wedge switch

P30
1 jersey 2 flags 3 birds 4 eyes
1 red 2 called 3 down 4 playing

1 sun, moon 4 pen, pencil
2 watch, clock 5 pages, words, pictures
3 children, people 6 egg, orange, apple

P31
1 blue, blew 2 I, eye 3 ate, eight
come, hum said, bed night, bite
meet, seat, bear, hair
plum